grade 2

For full details of exam requireme[nts] current syllabus in conjunctio[n] *Information & Regulations* and th[e] teachers and parents, *These Mus[...]* documents are available online at www.abrsm.org, as well as free of charge from music retailers, from ABRSM local representatives or from the Services Department, The Associated Board of the Royal Schools of Music, 24 Portland Place, London W1B 1LU, United Kingdom.

C000117745

CONTENTS

Where appropriate, pieces in this album have been checked with original source material and edited as necessary for instructional purposes. Fingering, metronome marks and the editorial realization of ornaments (where given) are for guidance only; they are not comprehensive or obligatory.

Editor for the Associated Board: **Richard Jones**

DO NOT PHOTOCOPY © MUSIC

Alternative pieces for this grade

Music origination by Barnes Music Engraving Ltd
Cover by Økvik Design
Printed in England by Headley Brothers Ltd,
The Invicta Press, Ashford, Kent

Rondo

A:1

BERTINI

Henri Bertini (1798–1876) was not only a French concert pianist and teacher, resident mainly in Paris, but also a prolific composer, whose best-known works are his piano studies. A rondo usually consists of a recurring theme interspersed with contrasting material (or episodes); this Rondo has just a single episode (bb. 9–12), which is followed by a varied reprise of the main theme.

Allegro grazioso

Second movement from Sonatina in C, Op. 57 No. 1

Edited by
Nancy and Randall Faber

BIEHL

Albert Biehl (1836–99) was a German composer who studied at the Leipzig Conservatory and wrote much piano music including several educational works, such as *The Elements of Piano Playing*, Op. 30, and the *New School of Velocity and Execution for the Piano Forte*, Op. 66.

AB 3387

Gypsy Dance

No. 6 from *Zingarese*, Hob. IX/28

Edited by
Otto Erich Deutsch

HAYDN

The eight *Zingarese per il Clavicembalo*, Hob. IX/28, believed to have been written by the great Austrian composer Joseph Haydn (1732–1809), are stylized Hungarian gypsy dances. All dynamics are editorial suggestions only.

All enquiries about this piece, apart from those directly relating to Zine exams, should be addressed to ABRSM (Publishing) Ltd, 24 Portland Place, London W1B 1LU.

AB 3387

Mazurka

from *Coppélia*

B:1

Arranged by
Daniel Scott

DELIBES

Léo Delibes (1836–91) was a French composer who studied at the Paris Conservatoire and worked as a church organist, as chorus master at the Paris Opéra, and later as professor of composition at the Conservatoire. His best-known works are the classical ballets *Coppélia* (1870), from which this piece is drawn, and *Sylvia* (1876), and his opera *Lakmé* (1883). The 'mazurka' is a triple-time dance of Polish origin.

© 1989 by Faber Music Ltd
Reproduced from *Play Romantic Paris* by permission of the publishers. All enquiries about this piece, apart from those directly relating to the exams, should be addressed to Faber Music Ltd, 3 Queen Square, London WC1N 3AU.

Allegro moderato

First movement from Sonatina in G, Op. 136 No. 2

REINECKE

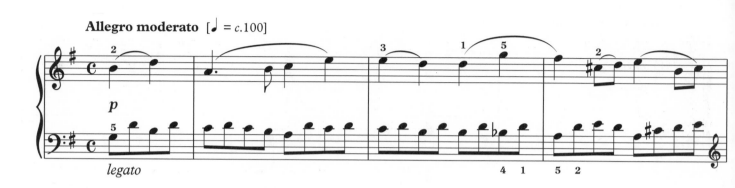

Carl Reinecke (1824–1910) was for many years conductor of the celebrated Leipzig Gewandhaus Orchestra. He was also professor of piano and composition, and later director, at the Leipzig Conservatory, where his pupils included Grieg and Sullivan. His huge output of compositions includes many piano pieces in the style of Schumann.

Source: *Sechs Miniatur-Sonaten*, Op. 136 (Leipzig: Breitkopf & Härtel, 1875)

The First Snowdrop

B:3

REIZENSTEIN

The German-born composer Franz Reizenstein (1911–68) studied composition with Hindemith in Berlin and later with Vaughan Williams in London, having emigrated to England in 1934. He was active not only as a composer but as a concert pianist and chamber musician, and during the last ten years of his life he was professor of piano at the Royal Academy of Music.

AB 3387

Wonderful Tonight

Arranged by
Julian McNamara

ERIC CLAPTON

Eric Clapton (b. 1945) is an English blues-rock guitarist. He formed the band Cream in 1966. Among his best-known songs are *Presence of the Lord*, *Tears in Heaven* and *Wonderful Tonight*, which is given here in a piano arrangement by Julian McNamara.

Mozzie

from *Easy Little Peppers*

C:2

ELISSA MILNE

Elissa Milne (b. 1967) is an Australian-born composer and piano teacher. She studied composition at the University of Auckland, performance studies and education at the University of Sydney, and arts management at the University of Technology, Sydney. She has written over 100 educational piano pieces. 'Mozzie' is written in a jazz-influenced style.

© 2004 by Faber Music Ltd

Reproduced from *Easy Little Peppers* by permission of the publishers. All enquiries about this piece, apart from those directly relating to the exams, should be addressed to Faber Music Ltd, 3 Queen Square, London WC1N 3AU.

Whistling Tune

GILES SWAYNE

The English composer Giles Swayne (b. 1946) studied with Raymond Leppard and Nicholas Maw at Cambridge, then at the Royal Academy of Music with Maw, Alan Bush and Harrison Birtwistle. He attended Messiaen's classes at the Paris Conservatoire in the late 1970s, and has since made prolonged visits to West Africa. He has written that 'Whistling Tune' 'should be played in a relaxed but jaunty manner, as if with hands in pockets (which would in fact be rather difficult)'.

Reproduced from *Spectrum 4: An International Collection of 66 Miniatures for Solo Piano* (ABRSM Publishing). All enquiries about this piece, apart from those directly relating to the exams, should be addressed to Gonzaga Music Ltd, 43 Victor Road, London NW10 5XB.

2/09

CONTENTS

Barbie
ANNUAL 2024

LittleBrother
BOOKS

Published 2023.
Little Brother Books Ltd, Ground Floor,
23 Southernhay East, Exeter, Devon EX1 1QL
books@littlebrotherbooks.co.uk | www.littlebrotherbooks.co.uk

Printed in China. EU Address: Korte Leemstraat 3, 2018 Antwerpen, Belgium

Barbie

DOUBLE THE FUN!

NAME: BARBIE ROBERTS

NICKNAME: MALIBU

BIRTHDAY: MARCH 9TH

STAR SIGN: PISCES

LIVES IN: CALIFORNIA AND NEW YORK

Malibu's friends...

'My friends in California are a pretty amazing crew. I've been friends with Daisy, Renee, Nikki and Teresa forever – but my oldest friend is Ken. He's also my next door neighbour!'

Malibu's family...

'I have three sisters: Skipper, Stacey and Chelsea. It can get a little crazy in our house sometimes, but we're always there for each other! My mum is a complete computer genius, and she also writes books, too – how cool is that? Dad makes documentaries so he's always asking questions about the world.'

Malibu loves...

TICK ALL THE THINGS YOU LOVE, TOO!

○ TECHNOLOGY

○ MUSIC

○ HER FRIENDS

○ HER FAMILY

○ FASHION

○ VLOGGING

○ READING

NAME: BARBIE ROBERTS

NICKNAME: BROOKLYN

BIRTHDAY: 13TH JULY

STAR SIGN: CANCER

LIVES IN: NEW YORK

Brooklyn's family...

'I live in Brooklyn with my amazing parents. Mum is an airline pilot, which keeps her pretty busy. She's always taught me to trust my instincts and make the right decisions. Dad's an architect, but his real passion is cooking. He makes the BEST dinners. I don't have any brothers or sisters, so meeting Malibu was like finding the sister I never had!'

Brooklyn loves...

TICK ALL THE THINGS YOU LOVE, TOO!

- ◯ SINGING
- ◯ DANCING
- ◯ PLAYING GUITAR
- ◯ SHOPPING
- ◯ GOING ON DAY TRIPS
- ◯ MEETING NEW PEOPLE
- ◯ MAKING PLANS

Brooklyn's friends...

'Our next-door neighbours Tyler and Emmitt adopted Jayla and Jackson when they were babies. They are the cutest twins you'll ever meet, but they can't help getting into mischief, especially when I am the one babysitting them!'

YOUR TURN

Now you know everything about **Brooklyn** and **Malibu**!
Use this page to create your very own profile – **all about you!**

NAME: ....

BIRTHDAY: ....

STAR SIGN: ....

LIVES IN: ....

....

My family...

Use this space to write the names of all the people you live with, spend time with and are part of your family. They can be aunts, uncles, cousins, grandparents or anyone who takes care of you.

✳ My friends...

Use this space to write the names of your favourite people.

NAME:

THEY ARE GREAT BECAUSE...

NAME:

THEY ARE GREAT BECAUSE...

NAME:

THEY ARE GREAT BECAUSE...

NAME:

THEY ARE GREAT BECAUSE...

♡ My favourite things ♡

ONE OF MY FAVOURITE FILMS IS:

I LIKE IT BECAUSE:

ONE OF MY FAVOURITE BOOKS IS:

I LIKE IT BECAUSE:

ONE OF MY FAVOURITE TV SHOWS IS:

I LIKE IT BECAUSE:

Three things that make me, me!

Use this space to name the three things you like most about yourself.

1

2

3

USE THIS SPACE TO DRAW A PICTURE OF YOURSELF!

TOTALLY 2024!

Use this page to plan out your **best year yet**. What will you get up to in **2024**? Keep your Annual safe, then remember to **tick** off everything you do at the end of the year.

THE FIRST BOOK I AM GOING TO READ THIS YEAR IS:

BY 2025 I WILL HAVE READ ☐ BOOKS!

THE SCHOOL SUBJECT I AM GOING TO TRY REALLY HARD AT THIS YEAR IS:

_____

_____

_____

THE FILM I WANT TO WATCH THIS YEAR IS:

THE HOBBY I WANT TO TRY / CONTINUE TO DO IS:

SURF ALL DAY

I'D LOVE TO GO ON A DAY TRIP TO:

I'D LOVE TO GO ON HOLIDAY TO:

FOR MY BIRTHDAY I WOULD LOVE TO:

FOR HALLOWEEN I WANT TO DRESS UP AS:

THE ONE THING I WANT TO DO IN SPRING IS:

THE ONE THING I WANT TO DO IN SUMMER IS:

THE ONE THING I WANT TO DO IN AUTUMN IS:

THE ONE THING I WANT TO DO IN WINTER IS:

CONCERT CHECKLIST

Malibu and **Brooklyn** are getting ready to showcase some new songs at a show.

Can you find every item on the list in the grid to make sure they are ready to perform? Look across, down and diagonally.

E	S	M	A	S	C	I	R	Y	L	L
E	B	P	R	A	D	E	R	M	A	A
D	T	I	E	L	D	A	Q	S	G	G
C	R	O	U	A	T	J	A	O	U	U
S	E	U	P	H	K	I	W	N	I	I
E	B	I	M	N	G	E	E	L	T	T
E	Y	B	O	S	B	B	R	E	A	A
W	A	T	E	R	M	A	L	I	R	R
B	U	F	D	V	B	H	U	T	S	S
M	I	C	R	O	P	H	O	N	E	E
U	W	E	D	F	G	T	Y	U	J	J
S	S	D	F	G	G	H	C	D	X	X
I	S	C	F	V	B	N	J	K	T	T
C	B	S	E	M	U	T	S	O	C	C
C	V	B	T	Y	U	J	K	M	I	I
S	O	N	G	L	I	S	T	G	H	H

☐ COSTUMES
☐ DRUMS
☐ GUITARS

☐ LYRICS
☐ MICROPHONE
☐ MUSIC

☐ SONG LIST
☐ SPEAKER
☐ WATER

Skater GIRL

Use the guide to help you complete this picture of Malibu performing an awesome skating trick with her equally sweet puppy!

MALIBU

1
2
3
4
5
6
7
8

DECIPHER YOUR DOODLES

SQUARES AND BOXES

Doodling squares can mean that you are great at getting things done. You would never leave homework to the last minute! If you drew a box, it could mean you have a birthday coming up – or there is something you are saving up for!

HOUSES

If you drew a house, it means you are feeling quite happy and settled right now – especially if the house you drew looks just like your own!

Use the space below to **doodle** anything you want for **60 seconds** (use a timer to help you – or just stop when you think you have drawn enough). Then, find out what your drawings say about you!

FLOWERS

What type of flowers did you doodle? If they are big and open, you are friendly and love meeting new people. If they are small, it could mean you like things to be organised and tidy.

HEARTS

You have a loving nature and love it when everyone gets along. You're the person your friends go to if they are feeling down.

SPIDERWEB

You might have a lot going on at the moment, or something big is coming up. Spiderwebs can mean you want to be more organised or you're wishing for something to happen.

BUTTERFLIES, LADYBIRDS OR BIRDS

Doodling creatures with wings could mean that you are looking for an adventure! You could be about to go away on holiday, or start a new club!

Chelsea's
BIRTHDAY SURPRISE

COLOUR A HEART
EVERY TIME YOU SPOT
A DIFFERENCE.

Malibu and her family have organised a surprise trip for Chelsea's birthday! Before they go, can you **find all six differences** between these pictures?

ANSWERS ON PAGE 76

BUDDY'S STILL BLOOMING!

Malibu, Brooklyn and Rafa were heading to Buddy's Café, their favourite place to eat. **'Since your last show, my phone has been blowing up!'** said Rafa. **'I've got a whole list of things for you guys to do before the next show.'**

Brooklyn peered over Rafa's shoulder to read his list. **'Done it, done that, and that,'** Brooklyn said. **'Oh, and done that too!'** said Malibu, giggling. **'Wow, it's like you guys don't even need me anymore,'** Rafa said, laughing nervously.

Inside Buddy's, the friends were shocked to see that all the booths were empty. **'It's been like this all week!'** Buddy cried. Epiphany comforted her boss. **'Don't worry, I'm sure things will pick up soon.'**

'This is serious!' said Malibu. **'What are we going to do?'** 'We need a big event to bring in the crowds,' said Brooklyn. **'We need to call Emmie!'** Emmie was Brooklyn's famous friend. She had thousands of fans online.

Emmie came as quickly as she could. **'Thank you so much!'** said Malibu. Rafa was just about to go and say hello, when he heard Brooklyn say something that stopped him in his tracks. **'By the way,'** said Brooklyn. **'I LOVE your manager!'** Rafa frowned. Maybe Brooklyn and Malibu really didn't need him any longer?

Emmie sat down in one of Buddy's booths with a chocolate cupcake and posted a selfie. Now, all they had to do was wait to see if it worked.

It only took an hour for Buddy's to be crammed with Emmie's fans, waiting to catch a glimpse of her. The queue to get in stretched along the street!

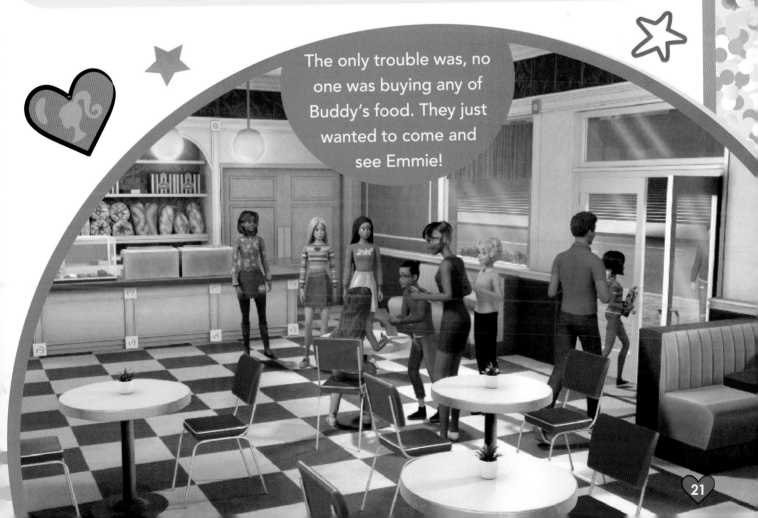

The only trouble was, no one was buying any of Buddy's food. They just wanted to come and see Emmie!

Just then, Malibu had a great idea. She ran outside to Emmie's queuing fans. **'Get your croissant signed by Emmie!'** she said. **'Fresh croissants sold inside!'** **'What a great idea!'** said Brooklyn. She's right, thought Rafa. A good manager would have come up with that idea first!

The croissants were a big success. **'I had to buy two!'** said one of Emmie's fans. **'One to eat and one to get signed.'**

A few hours later the queue was not any shorter, but the team had run into another problem. **'There's no food left!'** said Epiphany. **'Well, we'll just have to make some more, won't we?'** said Brooklyn.

'Erm, does anyone know how to use this thing?' asked Malibu, staring at the giant ovens in the kitchen. At that moment, their friend Stefan arrived. Stefan was great at mime acting – but Malibu wasn't so sure about his cooking skills.

As Brooklyn, Malibu and Stefan got to work in the kitchen, the crowds outside were getting tired… and hungry.

'OK,' said Brooklyn, when their baked creations had come out of the oven. 'I'm not sure what we've made, but it's definitely, something…'

'What's going on in there!' said Rafa through the kitchen door. 'We've made a sort of pastry...' said Brooklyn. 'Well, it could be more of a muffin...' said Malibu. 'Don't worry,' said Rafa, 'I got this.'

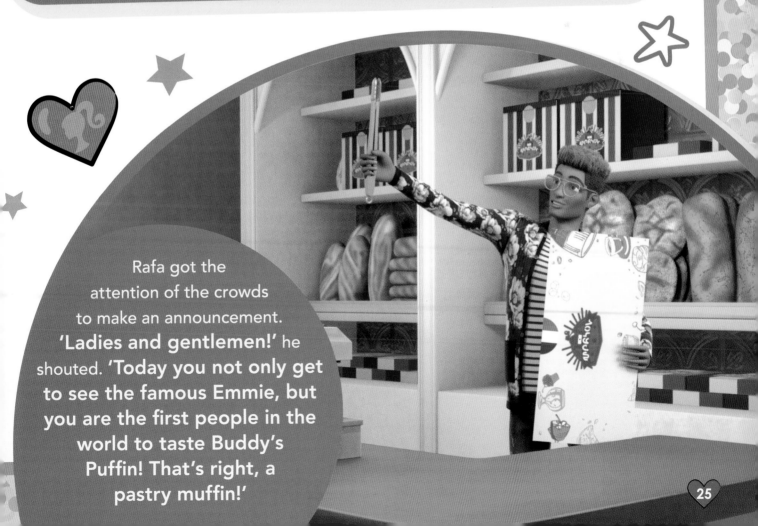

Rafa got the attention of the crowds to make an announcement. 'Ladies and gentlemen!' he shouted. 'Today you not only get to see the famous Emmie, but you are the first people in the world to taste Buddy's Puffin! That's right, a pastry muffin!'

The crowds loved the Puffin so much, they almost forgot that Emmie was there at all!

Buddy was delighted, and decided to make Puffins a regular on his menu. 'We make a pretty good team!' said Brooklyn. 'So, you're not going to swap me for Emmie's manager then?' asked Rafa. 'I heard you say how much you loved her.'

Brooklyn and Malibu looked at each other in disbelief. 'Rafa, we said we loved Emmie's MANICURE, not MANAGER!' Malibu said. 'You're not going anywhere,' said Brooklyn. 'Sorry!' 'Good,' said Rafa, relieved. 'Because there is no place I would rather be than with my girls!'

New wheels

Brooklyn and Malibu need to choose the perfect car for their road trip to California. Match each of the cars into pairs, then circle the odd one out to discover which one they have decided on!

A

B

C

D

E

F

G

ANSWERS ON PAGE 76

Bike RIDE BFFS

Where would you like to go on a bike ride? Colour in this picture, then imagine where Malibu and Brooklyn are cycling!

SISTERS FOREVER

This cute picture of **Skipper** and **Malibu** is **missing some important pieces**. Work out which ones complete the picture – and which ones are fakes!

ANSWERS ON PAGE 76

DORM-ROOM RACE

Malibu and **Brooklyn** are about to find out they are sharing a dorm room! Help each Barbie Roberts to find her way **through the maze to the room.**

START

FINISH

START

ANSWERS ON PAGE 76

SCAVENGER HUNT

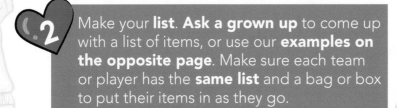

A scavenger hunt is a game where players race to find all the items on the list. Whoever completes their list first and gets back to 'base' is the winner.

1 Decide on a **base**. This is really important as it is **where you will start and end your hunt**. Living rooms are good for indoor games. Back doors or a park bench are good for an outdoor hunt.

2 Make your **list**. **Ask a grown up** to come up with a list of items, or use our **examples on the opposite page**. Make sure each team or player has the **same list** and a bag or box to put their items in as they go.

3 **Ready, steady, go!** Each player or team must **start at the same time**. Set a time limit for players to be back at base – even if they haven't got all the items on the list.

4 **Declare the winner!** The winner is the player or team that either gets the **most items on the list**, or completes the list in the **fastest time**. Make sure a grown up checks each list to make sure it is fair.

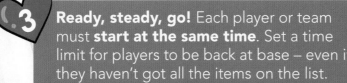

Malibu and her family love nothing more than a **scavenger hunt**! Read the instructions, then all you have to do is decide whether to play inside or outside!

INDOOR HUNT:

- A BOOK WITH MORE THAN 100 PAGES
- A TEDDY
- SOMETHING WITH WHEELS
- A TOOTHBRUSH
- SOMETHING BLUE
- SOMETHING THAT RATTLES
- A RULER
- A COIN

OUTDOOR HUNT:

- A BROWN ROCK
- A FEATHER
- A HEART-SHAPED LEAF
- A FLOWER
- SIX BLADES OF GRASS
- A GREY ROCK
- STICK
- A SEED

Make your own list here:

33

Christmas WRAPPED

Malibu has finished wrapping all her gifts, and they look just perfect! Take a look at the **shadows below**, which one matches Malibu perfectly?

A
B
C
D
E
F

ANSWERS ON PAGE 76

34

DANCING WITH STYLE

Brooklyn loves to dance, but which style is her favourite? Finish the picture by **joining up the dots** to reveal Brooklyn in her best dancing outfit.

WHAT'S YOUR FRIENDSHIP Superpower?

Each person has their own special **friend-power** – are you ready to find out yours? **Answer the questions to find out.**

IT'S LUNCHTIME AT SCHOOL, WHAT ARE YOU DOING?

a ORGANISING A GAME

b HELPING A FRIEND OUT WITH A PROBLEM

c TELLING JOKES TO MAKE YOUR FRIENDS LAUGH

WHO ARE YOU MOST LIKE?

a BROOKLYN

b MALIBU

c A BIT OF BOTH

WHICH OF THESE JOBS WOULD YOU LIKE THE MOST?

a TEACHER

b DOCTOR

c PERFORMER

TIME FOR A SLEEPOVER! WHAT'S YOUR JOB?

a SETTING OUT THE SLEEPING BAGS ○

b FINDING A SPECIAL SPOT FOR EVERYONE'S TEDDIES ○

c PICKING OUT THE FUNNIEST FILM TO WATCH ○

WHAT'S THE BEST THING ABOUT FRIENDSHIP?

a HELPING EACH OTHER ○

b HAVING SOMEONE TO TALK THINGS THROUGH WITH ○

c HAVING FUN TOGETHER ○

YOUR FRIEND HAS HAD SOME BAD NEWS, WHAT DO YOU DO?

a FIND OUT HOW YOU CAN HELP ○

b GIVE THEM A HUG ○

c TRY TO MAKE THEM SMILE ○

MOSTLY As:
SUPER SUPPORTER

When friends are in trouble, they know just who to call – you! Whether it's help with homework, a tricky decision to make, or a play to be watched, you're there.

Special abilities:
Cheering friends on in an extra loud voice!

MOSTLY Bs:
CARING COMFORTER

If a friend is upset, you're the person they go to. You're understanding, patient and you're always ready to listen.

Special abilities:
Super-charged hugging arms.

MOSTLY Cs:
CHAMPION CHEERER-UPPER

When friends are feeling down, you're great at cheering them up again. You are brilliant at making people laugh and seeing the bright side of any situation.

Special abilities:
Coming up with a joke at lightening speed!

Hairstyles

WITH MALIBU, BROOKLYN AND NIKKI!

SIDE PLAIT — This look is easy to achieve, with a bit of practice!

1. Brush your hair through if needed, then give yourself a centre parting.

2. Take a section of hair from the top of your head, to one side.

3. Divide that section into three and start to plait as neatly as you can (see below for our handy plaiting guide!)

4. Keep the plait as close to your hairline as possible, so that it lies over the top of the rest of your hair.

TOP BUN — The perfect style for dancing, sport, or if your hair needs a wash!

1. Brush your hair through if needed, or just gather your hair on the top of your head.

2. Scoop it into a high ponytail.

3. Twist the hair in your pony around itself until it starts to wrap around your hair tie, or simply comb until it looks neat.

4. Hold in place and secure with kirby grips all around the bun shape. If you don't have kirby grips, use another hair tie to keep your bun in place.

Four fabulous styles to inspire you!

HALF KNOT

Super easy and super stylish, too!

1. If your hair is braided like, start by gathering up a section of braids at the top of your head. If it is straight or wavy, use a brush to brush a section of hair at the top of your head into your hands.

2. Next, take a hair tie and make a pony tail on top of your head with the section you have just gathered.

3. Wind the hair inside the pony tail around until it starts to wrap around the hair tie.

4. Secure with another hair tie, or kirby grips if you have them.

DOUBLE BUN

A super cute style for double the fun!

1. For afro hair, start by dampening your hair a little with water or oil spray.

2. Comb your hair into two equal sections using a wide-tooth comb or your fingers.

3. Use large hair ties or elastic to make two ponytails on each side of your head.

4. Tease out sections of each ponytail to smooth over and tuck into the elastic or secure with a kirby grip until you have two smooth buns.

I'M IN THE BAND!

BAND NAME

BAND NAME PART ONE:

1	THE
2	HAPPY
3	SPARKLING
4	STRONG
5	DANCING
6	POWERFUL

BAND NAME PART TWO:

1	UNICORNS
2	SHOOTING STARS
3	LEADERS
4	MERMAIDS
5	QUEENS
6	DAREDEVILS

....

FIRST TRACK

Roll the dice three times to find the name of your first song. When you have it, why not have a go at writing your own song?

SONG NAME PART ONE:

1	FLYING
2	WALKING
3	SINGING
4	MOVING
5	RUNNING
6	SOARING

SONG NAME PART TWO:

1	INTO
2	OUT OF
3	OVER
4	UNDER
5	THROUGH
6	TOWARDS

SONG NAME PART THREE:

1	THE WORLD
2	THE STARS
3	FRIENDSHIP
4	THE FUTURE
5	THE PAST
6	FOREVER

....

Roll the dice to discover your band name, what you'll be in the band, and what your first song will be called!

YOUR ROLE

Will you be the singer? Drummer? Guitarist? Time to find out!

1	LEAD VOCALS
2	LEAD GUITAR
3	RHYTHM GUITAR AND VOCALS
4	DRUMMER
5	KEYBOARD
6	BASS GUITAR AND VOCALS

....

BAND LOGO

Use the space below to design your band logo, the cover of your first track or a picture of your band!

BE AN INVENTOR!

What would we do without the **internet**, the **television** or even the **wheel**? **Inventions** can change lives, so what could you invent? Use the page below to plan your **own invention!**

The idea

All inventions start with a single idea. Think about something in your life that you would like to be easier, or might help someone else!

The design

What will your invention look like? Is it sleek and pocket-sized, or big and bold with lots of different parts. Use this space and let your creativity flow!

GREAT INVENTIONS!

AQUARIUMS:
Jeanne Villepreux-Power wanted a way to study sea-life over a long period of time, so she invented the aquarium in 1832.

HOW ABOUT AN APP THAT CHOOSES YOUR OUTFIT FOR YOU EACH MORNING?

I'D INVENT A MACHINE THAT CLEANED STACIE'S SOCCER BOOTS WITHOUT ANYONE TOUCHING THEM!

GREAT INVENTIONS!

THE TELEPHONE: The first telephone was invented in 1876 by Alexander Graham Bell. The first words spoken on the telephone were: 'Mr Watson come here, I need to see you!'

GREAT INVENTIONS!

THE INTERNET: In 1989 a British scientist called Tim Berners-Lee created the World Wide Web. That's where we get the www. at the start of every web address.

GREAT INVENTIONS!

THE FRIDGE: Florence Parpat came up with the idea for the refrigerator in 1914 when people were still using boxes filled with ice to keep their food fresh.

Sell, sell, sell!

Imagine you are going to sell your invention. Fill in the sections below, ready for your invention to be released into the world!

NAME:

COST:

AVAILABLE AT:

YOU NEED THIS INVENTION BECAUSE:

POSING PETS

These chilled-out pups each have a **perfectly-matching partner**. Can you find the matching pairs, and all the odd-ones out, too?

WHICH OF THE PUPPY PALS ABOVE WOULD YOU LOVE TO HAVE AS YOUR PET?
DISCOVER WHAT THEIR NAME WOULD BE BY FINDING YOUR FIRST INITIAL IN THE CHART, BELOW.

A	POPPY	J	TRIXIE	S	STANLEY
B	PUDDING	K	REX	T	MATILDA
C	SNOWY	L	ROVER	U	HARRY
D	PATCH	M	DOLLY	V	SCOUT
E	BOBBY	N	BAILEY	W	SKEETER
F	GEORGIE	O	POPPET	X	FLUFFY
G	HOLLY	P	FREDDIE	Y	SALLY
H	CHARLIE	Q	REBEL	Z	LULU
I	JO JO	R	GATSBY		

ANSWERS ON PAGE 76

Brooklyn's BIG DAY

Brooklyn is taking part in a show jumping event and she has two ponies to ride. Use the **code** to work out their names.

Use the code
1 = a, 2 = b, 3 = c
to discover this pony's name!

11 9 18 9

....

A	B	C	D	E	F	G	H	I	J	K	L	M	N	O	P	Q	R	S	T	U	V	W	X	Y	Z
1	2	3	4	5	6	7	8	9	10	11	12	13	14	15	16	17	18	19	20	21	22	23	24	25	26

ANSWERS ON PAGE 76

This time, use the backwards alphabet to uncover the name of this sweet pony!

Q Z W V

....

A	B	C	D	E	F	G	H	I	J	K	L	M	N	O	P	Q	R	S	T	U	V	W	X	Y	Z
Z	Y	X	W	V	U	T	S	R	Q	P	O	N	M	L	K	J	I	H	G	F	E	D	C	B	A

FRIENDS, FLIPPED!

Malibu is trying to upload this picture, but it's been scrambled! Can you put it back together again before she posts?

ANSWERS ON PAGE 76

1 ·······
2 ·······
3 ·······
4 ·······
5 ·······
6 ·······

FREE-TIME FUN

Complete this grid with all the **fun hobbies** on the list. How many have you tried?

- BAKING
- CYCLING
- READING
- CAMPING
- YOGA
- SOCCER
- ART
- MUSIC

ANSWERS ON PAGE 77

BOREDOM-BUSTERS
Ever had one of those days when there's just **nothing to do?**
Malibu and her **sisters** have you covered!

BUILD A DEN!

Chelsea loves playing make-believe with her sisters, and one of the best ways to do this is by making a den! Grab some sofa cushions to make walls, then drape blankets or bedsheets over the top to make the roof. Ask a grown-up to help you secure the den with clothes pegs.

PLAY THE FLOOR IS LAVA!

This is a great way to get active if its rainy and cold outside. Find a safe playing area, then place cushions on the floor between sofas and chairs. The aim of the game is to get safely from one side of the room to the other without touching the floor! Make sure you ask a grown-up if the room is safe to start before you begin playing.

MOVIE MARATHON

The rules for this one are simple. Everyone gets to pick their favourite movie! To make it fair, put the names of each friend or family member into a bowl and pick them out at random to see who gets to go first. Make sure you have a comfy place to sit and plenty of popcorn, too.

PEN AND PAPER GAMES

Although she's a whizz with technology, Malibu can create a fun games night with just a pen and paper. Try these three games below:

DOTS & SQUARES

Draw a grid of dots 10 across by 10 down. On each turn, players get to draw a line between the dots, either up and down, or left to right (never diagonally). If you draw a line that completes a square, you get to put your initials inside. The player with the most completed squares, wins!

SILLY STORY

The first player must write the first line of a story on the top of a piece of paper, then fold it over. The next player must write the second line, then fold it over. Carry on until you reach the last player who must write the end of the story. Unfold your piece of paper and read your silly story aloud!

CRAZY CHARACTER

Now it's time to test your drawing skills! The first player must secretly draw a head on the top of a piece of paper, then fold it over so the next player can't see. The next player draws the top of a body and arms, and folds it over again. Keep going until you reach the feet, then open up your drawing to see what your character looks like! You can draw anything you want, from an alien's head to a fish tail. The sillier the better.

SEA, SAND AND SEARCH!

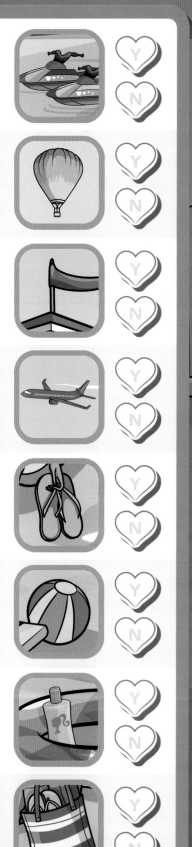

Take a look at the smaller pictures at the side of the page, can you **spot** them all in this beach scene? Place a **tick** next to each one you find. Watch out! Some of the pictures don't fit!

ANSWERS ON PAGE 77

DESIGNER DINER

Buddy's café has just employed two new waitresses, and they need uniforms! Create two new designs for Brooklyn and Malibu before they get to work.

PATTERN

What type of patterns do you like best? Spots, stripes and florals are fun – but do they work for your uniform design?

COLOUR

Do you want your uniforms to be crisp and clean or to stand out from the crowd? Will Brooklyn and Malibu match? Why not test your ideas on a blank piece of paper first.

FABRIC

The best designers always consider fabric. Will it be stretchy or stiff? Cotton or wool? Think about your comfiest clothes. What are they made out of?

The Copy Cat

It was the day of the school portrait competition and Barbie had just been awarded first prize. **'Thank you, Principal Millar!'** Barbie replied, accepting the trophy.

'Urgh, she wins again!' said Tammy, angrily. **'Why is it always Barbie, Barbie, Barbie? What do I have to do to get some attention?'** Just then, Tammy came up with an idea. If she wanted to get attention like Barbie, maybe she had to be JUST LIKE Barbie?

Back at home, the Roberts' friend, Casey was dropping off her pet Macaw. **'Thank you so much for taking care of Bella while I am away,'** she said. Stacie and Chelsea took the bird excitedly. They couldn't wait to look after another pet. **'Don't worry,'** said Stacie. **'She's in safe hands.'**

The next day, Tammy arrived at school to give Barbie a big surprise. Tammy had bought a dress just like Barbie's, she was wearing a blonde wig and even driving the exact same car! **'So, what do you think?'** said Tammy, grinning.

Stacie and Chelsea were having such a fun time looking after Bella. She was a very good bird, so they didn't think anything of leaving her while they popped into the kitchen to have lunch. When they came back into the living room, they were in for a shock. **'The cage is open!'** said Stacie. **'So's the back door!'** said Chelsea.

Next door, it was Poppy Reardon's birthday. Although she had received lots of wonderful presents from her husband, Whitaker, she was most excited to see what her son, Trey, had got her.

Trey shifted from foot to foot. He had completely forgotten his mother's birthday! Just then, Bella flew through the door. **'Who is this adorable creature?'** Poppy asked. **'She's your birthday present!'** Trey replied, thinking quickly.

'Who's a pretty girl?' squawked Bella, to Poppy's delight. **'She's the best present ever!'**

Tammy had been copying Barbie all day. Barbie was just about to start taking donations for a tree-planting ceremony at school, when she saw that Tammy had beaten her to it. **'Are you copying me to get the award for the most donations?'** Barbie asked. **'I'm just being more Barbie!'** replied Tammy.

At the tree planting ceremony, everyone had gathered to see how much money had been raised, and how many trees they were going to plant. **'Well done everyone!'** Principle Millar said. **'Especially... Tammy!'** Although Barbie was disappointed not to win, she clapped as Tammy received her award.

Stacie and Chelsea had searched all over the neighbourhood for Bella. They were just about to give up when they heard Bella's distinctive squawk coming from inside the Reardon's house! **'They have Bella!'** said Chelsea. **'We've got to help her,'** said Stacie.

That afternoon, Barbie went to the stables for her riding lesson. She sighed when she saw that Tammy was already there. **'I didn't know you could ride a horse,'** Barbie said. **'Huh, how hard can it be?'** said Tammy.

59

Barbie frowned. 'Tammy, you do know this is the advanced lesson, don't you?' she asked as Tammy struggled to get into the saddle. 'Anything you can do, I can do too!' Tammy said.

Tammy and Barbie entered the horse training yard. Barbie trotted confidently as Tammy struggled to keep up. Suddenly, Tammy's horse took off, knocking Tammy to the floor.

After the lesson, Barbie found Tammy back in the stable yard. She looked miserable. **'Are you OK?'** she asked. **'I guess it's harder than I thought, being as awesome as Barbie all the time,'** Tammy replied. **'But there's so much that's awesome about you,'** Barbie said, kindly. **'You just have to be you.'**

Just then, Barbie's phone rang. **'Stacie? What? Casey's Macaw is at the Reardon's? I'll be right there!' 'Maybe I can help,'** says Tammy. **'I know quite a bit about birds...'**

Tammy and Barbie headed back to Barbie's neighbourhood. They knocked on the Reardon's door. **'Just follow my lead!'** Tammy said, giving Barbie a wink. **'Hello, Mrs Reardon,'** Tammy said cheerfully. **'Trey told us all about your new bird, may we come in?'**

Inside, Tammy began telling Mrs Reardon all about Macaws. **'And did you know they can live for up to 80 years?'** she said. **'80 years!'** Poppy said, horrified. **'Urgh! Take the creature away. I can't look after a pet for that long!'**

Stacie and Chelsea cheered as Tammy brought Bella back into the house. 'Well done, Tammy!' they said. Tammy looked at Barbie, a little shyly. 'Barbie, why were you so kind to me when I have spent the week copying you?' 'It's just who I am,' said Barbie. Tammy smiled. 'Maybe the one thing I can carry on copying is your kindness,' she said.

COPY CAT QUIZ

Now you have read **The Copy Cat**, what can you remember?
See if you can **answer** all of the **questions**.

1 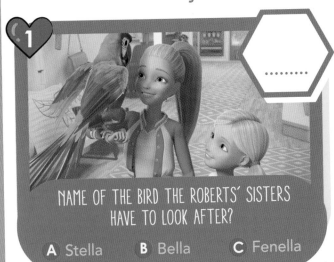 ....

NAME OF THE BIRD THE ROBERTS' SISTERS HAVE TO LOOK AFTER?

A Stella **B** Bella **C** Fenella

2 ....

WHAT IS TAMMY COLLECTING DONATIONS FOR?

D A tree-planting ceremony
E A sponsored silence
F An animal shelter

3  ....

WHO WINS THE PORTRAIT CONTEST?

G Tammy **H** Barbie **I** Trey

4  ....

WHO DOES TREY GIVE CASEY'S MACAW TO?

J His father **K** His friend **L** His mother

5  ....

WHO HELPS TO GET THE BIRD BACK?

M Trey **N** Ken **O** Tammy

6  ....

WHO FALLS OFF THEIR HORSE?

P Tammy **Q** Barbie **R** Stacie

ANSWERS ON PAGE 77

CRACKED UP

Malibu has damaged her phone screen! Can you help her to discover who is calling?

1

2

3

4

ANSWERS ON PAGE 77

BROOKLYN'S BUDDY

Help Brooklyn to get to her puppy! Each number equals a minute. Add the numbers along the paths to find the quickest route through the park!

A
B
C

7
8
3
4
8
3
2
5
2
1
1

ANSWERS ON PAGE 77

SISTER'S SEQUENCE

Malibu is helping Chelsea to tidy her room. Can you work out which item comes next in each sequence?

ANSWERS ON PAGE 77

Family tree

Grandpa Roberts

Chelsea

Stacie

Grandma Roberts

Blissa

Taffy

Dad

Skipper

Mum

Barbie 'Malibu' Roberts

Family is super important to Malibu. **Take a look at her tree**, full of all the important people in her life, then fill yours in, too! Your tree can be filled with **family members**, **people you live with**, or anyone **who cares for you!**

COSTUME PARTY

Everyone has chosen their costumes for a **fancy-dress party!**
Take a closer look at each of these outfits. **Spot** the clues,
then draw lines to match each person to their costume.

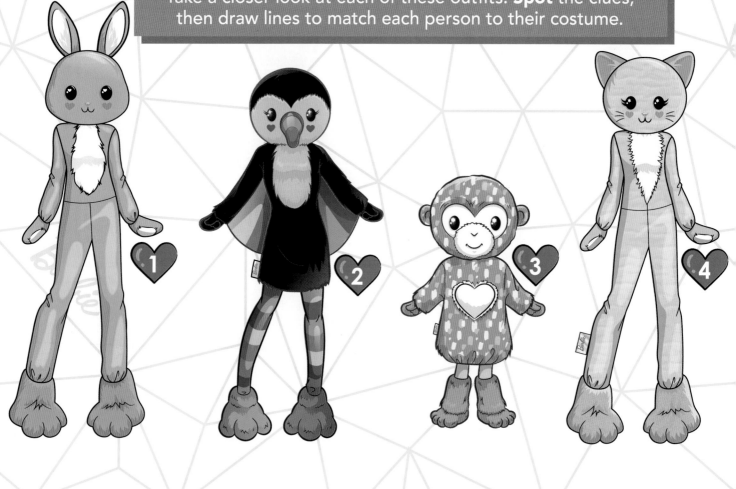

1   2   3   4

A   B   C   D

ANSWERS ON PAGE 77

Squad goals

Malibu and Brooklyn can do anything with their pals by their side!

COSY CUPS

When it's chilly outside, there's nothing better than **cuddling up with a mug of something yummy!**

Ask an adult for help.

Home-made hot chocolate

Recipe

○ 250 ml of a milk of your choice

○ 25 g of your favourite chocolate (milk, dark or white)

○ 1 tsp of cocoa (if you have it)

What to do

Ask an adult to gently heat the milk in a pan. Stir in the chocolate until it is completely melted. Add the cocoa once all the chocolate has mixed with the milk, then pour into your favourite mug. Add some whipped cream and marshmallows if you have them!

Lush lemon and honey

Recipe

- ◯ Half a lemon
- ◯ One teaspoon of honey

What to do

Ask a grown up to boil the kettle for you, then let it cool for a minute or two. While you wait, carefully slice your lemon into thin, round slices. Pop your lemon and honey into a mug, then pour over the hot water and stir until the honey has dissolved. This drink is great if you have a cold, too!

Ask an adult for help.

Apple & cinnamon sparkle

Recipe

- ◯ 200 ml apple juice
- ◯ 50 ml water
- ◯ One cinnamon stick
- ◯ Thin apple rounds (optional)

What to do

Gently heat the apple juice and water on the stove with the cinnamon stick. While it heats, thinly slice some apple into rounds. Ask a grown up to help you pour the apple juice into a mug (remove the cinnamon stick first!) then add the apple slices. The perfect wintery treat!

Ask an adult for help.

FRIENDSHIP FOREVER

Brooklyn and **Malibu** know how important their friends are. Read all about their special friendships and fill in your **own friendship factfiles**.

Lyla

It took a little while, but Brooklyn and Malibu soon won over this super-tough rock chick. As well as looking after Blown Speaker studios where the girls record their music, Lyla has become a true friend – just never ask her to listen to pop music.

Rafa

When Malibu and Brooklyn moved to New York, they not only found each other – they found Rafa, too! Their mutual BFF as well as being their official costume designer and all round advice-giver. The girls would not know what to do without him.

Ken Carson

Ken is Malibu's oldest friend and probably knows her better than anyone. He lives next door to the Roberts' in California and loves spending time at the beach, in fact, he's training to be a lifeguard!

Epiphany

As well as serving the girls in Buddy's Diner, Epiphany's kind heart and warm personality meant they were destined to become friends. Epiphany believes everything has an aura and a personality – which is why she once believed the chairs in the diner were bored!

Teresa

If Malibu ever needs a sensible, level-headed opinion, Teresa is her friend of choice. Teresa is smart, hard-working and passionate – and a self-confessed science geek!

Renee

Renee is Malibu's sportiest friend. She loves anything from soccer to skateboarding, but her real passion is going really fast – on anything! She misses Malibu when she is in New York, but still stops by the Roberts' house to kick a ball with Skipper.

Friendship files

MY BEST FRIENDS ARE:

FRIENDS ARE IMPORTANT BECAUSE:

MY FUNNIEST FRIEND IS:

MY MOST CARING FRIEND IS:

I THINK I AM A GOOD FRIEND BECAUSE:

ANSWERS

PAGE 12

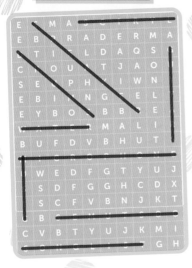

PAGE 16

PAGE 28

PAGE 30

PAGE 31

START

FINISH

START

PAGE 34

PAGE 44

PAGE 45

KIRI

JADE

PAGE 46

PAGE 47

baking
music
cycling
yoga
amping
ading

PAGE 50-51

PAGE 64

	B		D
1		2	

NAME OF THE BIRD THE ROBERTS' SISTERS HAVE TO LOOK AFTER?
A Stella B Bella C Fenella

WHAT IS TAMMY COLLECTING DONATIONS FOR?
D A tree planting ceremony E A sponsored silence F An animal shelter

3	H	4	L

WHO WAS THE PORTRAIT STYLIST?
G Tammy H Barbie I Trey

WHO DOES TREY GIVE CASEY'S MACAW TO?
J His father K His friend L His mother

5	O	6	P

WHO HELPS TO GET THE BIRD BACK?
M Trey N Ken O Tammy

WHO FALLS OFF THEIR HORSE?
P Tammy Q Barbie R Stacie

PAGE 65

1 — BROOKLYN
2 — RAFA
3 — LYLA
4 — EPIPHANY

PAGE 66

A
B
C

PAGE 67

PAGE 70

1 C
2 A
3 D
4 B

77